Dear _____,

These are my wishes for you
today, tomorrow, always,
and no matter what...

In these tender times,
please know how very

_____

you are.

I know
you're struggling
right now,

and things
may feel
overwhelming
and dark.

Maybe even

_____ .

I want you to know:

in these times,

when it's hard for you

to see very far into the distance,

that I _____.

You've generously shared your light

and your _____

with me and many others—

and now I'm ready, willing, and able

to help light your way.

I know what

the brightest parts of you are like.

I have seen your inner spark, and it

_____.

I remember
what is possible for you

even when you forget.

I have long kept a list

in my heart

of things

I appreciate
and admire
about you,

like your

_____

and your _____ .

I know how

_____

you are.

I know how much you take on

and how much you

_____.

You deserve

_____.

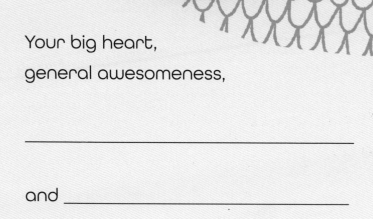

Your big heart,
general awesomeness,

_____

and _____

are a part of you.

And you can't lose them.

They are the essence of you,
woven into the fabric of you,
and they are always with you.

No storm can wash away
who you are.

No night is dark enough

to extinguish your

_____ .

The stars wouldn't allow it,

and neither will I.

May you remember

that you are not a burden.

You are human,

and one of

my favorite humans

of all time.

I know
you will find your way.

And until you do, we can

_____.

When you are at full capacity,

I will help you

_____.

You do not have to
carry all of this yourself—

no matter
what "this"
may be.

Please know that
I am not afraid of the dark,
and I am here
to light your way

until your own flame
burns brightly again. And I'll bring

_____ .

Believe this:

It is easy to love you.

You are so lovable,

and you are so

_____

to me.

Love,

_____